BEAU PEEP

BY ROGER KETTLE & ANDREW CHRISTINE

AN EXPRESS BOOKS PUBLICATION

Printed by Eyre & Spottiswoode, Cosham, Hants. & co-ordinated by Roeder Print Services Ltd.

£1.75

CONFIDENTIAL:– DOCTOR'S REPORT
SUBJECTS:– ROGER KETTLE AND
ANDREW CHRISTINE

This is indeed a baffling case. The photograph shows the two patients halfway up an alley indulging in what appears to be a silly-face contest. I can see no hope of these people living a normal life. As they seem to be completely harmless, my recommendation is that they be allowed to continue doing their little drawings of funny men in funny hats.

DOCTOR Z. McLUNIE
(HEAD OF PSYCHIATRY).

THE ADVENTURES OF LEGIONNAIRE

BEAU PEEP

FROM THE STAR

SIGH!
1624

HAVE YOU GOT YOUR HARMONICA, DENNIS?
YES.

PLAY THAT SONG FOR ME.
WHAT SONG?

THAT SONG THAT TEARS AT MY HEART... THAT SPEAKS FOR A MILLION LONELY PEOPLE...

...THAT SONG FOR - SNIFF - THOSE OF US WHO HAVE LOVED AND LOST...

I CAN ONLY DO "KNEES UP MOTHER BROWN."

HALT!

TELL HIM THIS IS THE LAND OF OUR FATHERS...

...THAT THE FREEDOM TO ENJOY IT RESTS WITH OUR PEOPLE, AND OUR PEOPLE ALONE.

TELL HIM THAT IT IS FORBIDDEN FOR HIM TO WALK THIS LAND BY ANCIENT LAWS.

YOU'RE NICKED, SQUIRE.

ALL THE BEST, DENNIS!
CHEERS, BEAU!
1654

IT'S NICE TO BE ABLE TO CELEBRATE SOMETHING...

...INSTEAD OF JUST BOOZING AWAY FOR NO REASON.

IT MAKES IT ALL THE MORE SPECIAL.

SO, DENNIS, LET US CHARGE OUR GLASSES AGAIN AND DRINK TO—

—HOW OLD IS YOUR MUM'S BUDGIE AGAIN?

ALL RIGHT, I'M COMING!

THERE'S NO NEED TO SHOUT!

ALL DAY LONG— NAG, NAG, NAG!

IT'S A WONDER I DON'T GO STARK, STARING MAD WORKING HERE.
1630

AND, ANYWAY, WHAT DO YOU KNOW? YOU'RE JUST A POTATO.

THAT RIFLE IS FILTHY, PEEP!
1642

LOOK AFTER HIM AND HE'LL LOOK AFTER YOU...

...TAKE CARE OF HIM AND HE'LL NEVER LET YOU DOWN.

SO, REMEMBER, TREAT IT LIKE YOUR BEST FRIEND!

FANCY A DRINK IN THE PUB?

JUST LOOK AT YOURSELF, EGON!
1785

HOW CAN YOU SERVE FOOD LIKE THAT!

OH, I SEE! MY LACE IS UNDONE!

EGON! **TSK!** WHERE IS THAT SCRUFF?
1786

YOU RANG, SIR?
YES, EGON, I'D LIKE A...

...LIKE A...

...LIKE A NEW PAIR OF GLASSES.

WHAT DO YOU THINK, THEN?
AMAZING! YOU LOOK ABSOLUTELY FABULOUS, EGON!
1787

I THOUGHT IT WAS TIME TO SHOW YOU I WAS A MAN OF REFINEMENT AND CULTURE.

GET YOUR *!! ☆◎ ELBOW OFF THE TABLE!

I'M CRACKING UP!

IT'S NOT NATURAL TO BE CLEAN AND TIDY!
1788

GLOOP!

I NEEDED THAT!

I SEE THE NEW IMAGE IS SLOWLY SLIPPING AWAY.
1789

I FEEL SO RESTRICTED WHEN I'M ALL DRESSED UP.

I'M SURE MY COOKING IS BEGINNING TO SUFFER.

LOOK AT THAT! MY RICE PUDDINGS HAVE GONE TO HELL!

THAT'S IT! I'M BACK TO NORMAL!
1790

YOU CAN'T HIDE YOUR REAL SELF BEHIND FANCY CLOTHES!

I THINK YOU'LL FIND THE HONESTY REFLECTED IN MY COOKING.

WHAT IS IT?
I HONESTLY HAVEN'T A CLUE.

I DOUBT IF I'LL BE ABLE TO GET RID OF THIS JUNK.
HONEST ABDUL
1791

WAIT! MY POCKET'S TINGLING. THERE'S A MUG AROUND SOMEWHERE!

DRAT! I USED TO BE ABLE TO TOUCH MY NOSE WITH MY TONGUE!

A CUSTOMER— AND IT'S THAT IDIOT WHO BOUGHT STUFF BEFORE!
NEST ABDUL
1792

GREETINGS, FRIEND! I TRUST YOU'VE HEARD OF ALADDIN?
THE BOLTON LEFT-HALF?

I LOVE YOU.

THAT'S ALL I HAVE TO DO?
YEP!
ABDUL
1793

JUST RUB THE LAMP AND YOUR WISH WILL BE INSTANTLY GRANTED!

COO! THANKS, MATE!
HANG ON A MINUTE!

DO YOU...ER ...HAVE ANY BROTHERS?

LOOK WHAT I BOUGHT FROM HONEST ABDUL– A MAGIC LAMP!
1794

IF I RUB IT, ANY WISH I MAKE COMES TRUE!

RUB! RUB!

ASK FOR A BRAIN.

DENNIS, YOU'VE BEEN CONNED— THAT'S NOT A MAGIC LAMP!
1795

IT IS TOO! IT'LL MAKE MY WISHES COME TRUE!

RUB! RUB! RUB!

I TAKE IT YOU ASKED FOR BLISTERS.

I'LL SHOW YOU THIS LAMP WORKS!
RUB! RUB!
1796

EXCUSE ME—IS THE COLONEL IN?
RUB! RUB!
DENNIS! I TAKE IT ALL BACK! IT DOES WORK!

I ASKED FOR A COWBOY HAT.

MY OLD FOOTBALL BOOTS!

I WONDER HOW MANY GOALS THESE FAITHFUL LITTLE BEAUTIES POPPED IN?
1797

AH, YES – I REMEMBER IT NOW.

...1,426...
1798

THAT'S THE 1426TH. CONSECUTIVE TIME I'VE FAILED TO KEEP THE BALL UP MORE THAN ONCE.

AND IT'S PEEP OF ENGLAND ON THE BALL...
...HE'S ONLY GOT THE BRAZILIAN KEEPER TO BEAT!
SHUFFLE!
1799

BUT WAIT! HE'S SPUN ROUND AND BACK HEELED THE WINNER! THE MAN'S A GENIUS!
BOP!

I HAVE TO SAY, PEEP, THAT THERE ARE TIMES WHEN YOU WORRY ME.

WILL YOU HELP ME WITH MY TRAINING, DENNIS?
OKAY!
1800

I'LL THROW THE BALL TO YOU AND YOU HEAD IT.
RIGHT!

IS THAT IT?

TRY TO TAKE THE BALL OFF ME, DENNIS!
JINK!

IMPOSSIBLE, EH? YOU'RE DAZZLED BY THE SHEER BRILLIANCE OF THE FOOTWORK! YOU'RE A BEMUSED FULL-BACK!
SHIMMY!

I'M A GOALIE.
1801

WELL, YOU CAN'T PLAY 'COS IT'S MY BALL!
DON'T CARE!
1802

I BET YOU DO!
I BET I DON'T!

'COS YOU WON'T GET TO PLAY WITH MY CRAYONS!
DON'T CARE!

PLEASE GOD LET NOBODY EVER ATTACK US!

AHA! A LONE VULTURE!
1803

I'VE ALWAYS FELT A STRANGE BOND WITH THESE CREATURES.

BOTH OUTCASTS, WE STRUGGLE FOR SURVIVAL IN A HOSTILE ENVIRONMENT.

A MILLION SQUARE MILES OF DESERT AND THIS NUTCASE FINDS ME.

HOW WOULD YOU LIKE TO BE MY SPECIAL FRIEND?
NO THANKS.
1804

YOU'D LIKE THAT, WOULDN'T YOU?
NO.

YOU KNOW I COULD SWEAR THERE'S A FLICKER OF INTELLIGENCE BEHIND THOSE EYES.
THAT'S A DAMN SIGHT MORE THAN CAN BE SAID FOR YOU, SUNBEAM.

I THINK I'LL GIVE YOU A NAME.
SPARE ME.
1805

I BET IT'S "VIC." IT'S ALWAYS "VIC." "VIC" THE VULTURE. I HATE "VIC."

THE PATHETIC THING IS HE'LL BE PROUD OF HIMSELF.

I'VE GOT IT! I'VE GOT IT! VIC!

I'VE GOT A GOOD IDEA, VIC!
I DOUBT IT.
1806

I'M GOING TO TEACH YOU SOME TRICKS!
YOU JEST.

WHEN I THROW THIS STICK, YOU FETCH IT!
DON'T HOLD YOUR BREATH.

READY?
THE MAN'S AN IDIOT.
1807

FETCH!
WHAT DOES HE THINK I'D WANT WITH A STICK?

DON'T YOU UNDERSTAND?
PERFECTLY. YOU'RE A HALF-WIT.

I FEEL I CAN TALK TO YOU, VIC...
OH, NO.
1808

I CAN HANDLE ANYTHING BUT THE LIFE STORY.

I WAS BORN-
YOU GOT ME IN THE EYE THERE, VIC.

THIS WILL BE A FULL-SCALE EXERCISE.
1809

ONE GROUP WILL BE 'X', THE OTHER 'O'. NOTHING SIMPLER!

WHAT'S AN 'O'?

YOU'RE AN 'X' AND I'M AN 'O'...
1810

...WE SPLIT UP, MERGE INTO THE DESERT AND, USING OUR SURVIVAL INSTINCTS CAPTURE EACH OTHER!

HIDE AND SEEK, DENNIS.

WE SPLIT UP FOR THE EXERCISE NOW, DENNIS.
1811

ALL YOU HAVE TO DO IS AVOID BEING CAUGHT BY THE 'O's.

DON'T BE SMUTTY, DENNIS.

I LOVE THESE EXERCISES—THE 'X's AGAINST THE 'O's!
1812

IT'S MAD PIERRE AND HE'S AN 'X'! HERE'S MY CHANCE...

...TO AVOID CONCUSSION.

BANG! YOU'RE DEAD DENNIS!
NO, I'M NOT.
1813

YES, YOU ARE! YOU'RE AN 'X' AND I'M AN 'O' AND I SHOT YOU!

THE BULLET HIT MY BUTTON AND BOUNCED BACK AND KILLED YOU.

YOU'RE SO CHILDISH, DENNIS!

IT SEEMED LIKE A GOOD IDEA...
1814

...SPLIT THE MEN INTO TWO GROUPS, STAGE A MOCK BATTLE...

THAT'S IT! I'M NOT PLAYING IF YOU DON'T GO DEAD!
DON'T PLAY THEN, SISSY!

THIS HAS ALL THE MAKINGS OF A "TWO BOTTLES OF BRANDY" NIGHT.

NAUGHTY BOY! YOU'RE FISHING TO SEE WHAT I NEED FOR CHRISTMAS!

I LIKE TO DRESS UP AT CHRISTMAS TO CHEER UP THE MEN!
1817

BUT, SIR, IT ISN'T—
NECESSARY? I KNOW...

...BUT WHAT KIND OF COLONEL DOESN'T GIVE HIS MEN A TREAT AT THIS TIME OF YEAR?
PROD!

CHRISTMAS WAS MONTHS AGO, SIR.
WHAT?

YOU SAID YOU DRESSED UP 'COS IT'S CHRISTMAS— WELL, IT ISN'T.
1818

ER... WHY DON'T YOU LIE DOWN FOR A WHILE, SIR?
ALL RIGHT...

...SANTA WON'T COME IF I'M STILL UP!

HAVE YOU SEEN THE COLONEL?
NO.
1819

HE'S WANDERING AROUND DRESSED AS A FAIRY SHOUTING "MERRY CHRISTMAS."

OH, WAIT A MINUTE— HAS HE GOT A WAND?

YES HE HAS. FOOLISHLY I THOUGHT "DRESSED AS A FAIRY SHOUTING 'MERRY CHRISTMAS'" WOULD BE ENOUGH TO JOG YOUR MEMORY.

IT'S FRIGHTENING— OUR LIVES DEPEND ON THE COLONEL...

...AND HE DOESN'T EVEN KNOW WHAT DAY IT IS!
1820

IT'S NOVEMBER, ISN'T IT?

NO, PEEP, YOU CAN'T BUY YOUR WAY OUT OF THE LEGION.

D'YOU FANCY A GAME OF DARTS, BEAU?
STAR

I MUST WARN YOU, DENNIS, DOWN MY WAY I WAS KNOWN AS THE "BULLSEYE KID"!
STAR
1821

EAT A LOT OF SWEETS, DID YOU?

LET'S SEE IF MY TOUCH IS STILL THERE.
1822

NAME ANY DOUBLE, DENNIS!

WHISKEY!

HOW MANY DO I NEED, BEAU?
501.
1823

HOW MANY DO I NEED NOW?

501.

YOU NEED DOUBLE ELEVEN, DENNIS.
WHERE'S THAT?
1824

HANG ON—I'LL SHOW YOU.

IT'S THAT LITTLE RED—GET THE DOCTOR, DENNIS.

THROWING A DART IS A SIMPLE SCIENCE, DENNIS...
1825

...INCORPORATING THE TIMING OF RELEASE, THE ANGLE OF FLIGHT AND THE VELOCITY OF PROJECTILE.

GET THE DOCTOR, DENNIS.

GET THE DOCTOR, DENNIS.
1826

YOU HAVEN'T HURT YOURSELF PLAYING DARTS AGAIN ?
NO, I HAVEN'T...

...BUT I'M GOING TO NEED THE DOCTOR IN ABOUT 30 SECONDS.

PIERRE HAS GONE ABSENT WITHOUT LEAVE.

FIND HIM AND BRING HIM BACK— BY FORCE IF NECESSARY!
1827

YOU WANT *ME* TO FORCE MAD PIERRE TO COME BACK?
YES.

PERMISSION TO BLUBBER LIKE A BABY, SIR?

IT'S SIMPLE, BEAU— ALL YOU HAVE TO DO IS GO UP TO MAD PIERRE...
1828

...AND SAY "*YOU'RE ABSENT WITHOUT LEAVE. BACK TO THE FORT* ***NOW!***

THEN I'LL ASK FOR MY FINGER BACK.

IT'S MAD PIERRE— I KNEW HE'D BE HERE.
BAR

I'LL TAKE A DEEP BREATH THEN TELL HIM HE'S DUE BACK AT THE FORT *IMMEDIATELY!*
1829

I THINK I'LL WAIT TILL HE'S FINISHED TRYING TO PUSH THE BARMAN INTO THAT ICE-BUCKET.

HELLO, PIERRE!
WHAT DO *YOU* WANT?

WELL...ER...YOU'RE A BIT LATE FOR DUTY AND I'VE COME TO TAKE...ER...ASK YOU TO COME BACK, PLEASE...
1830
CAN I ASK YOU A QUESTION?
SURE.

DO YOU LIKE BREATHING?
WHY DON'T YOU STAY HERE?

YOU'VE GOT TO COME BACK, PIERRE— YOU'RE ABSENT WITHOUT LEAVE!

I MUST WARN YOU THE SERGEANT TOLD ME TO USE FORCE IF NECESSARY...

WHACK!
1831

...THOUGH, PERSONALLY, I'M AGAINST IT.

ALL RIGHT—I'LL COME BACK TO THE FORT.
YOU WILL?

YEAH, I WASN'T REALLY A.W.O.L.— IT'S JUST THAT SOMETIMES THINGS GET ON TOP OF ME...
1832

AND YOU NEEDED A QUIET DRINK TO SORT THINGS OUT?

NO, I NEEDED TO PUNCH BARMEN.

I'M FED UP WITH FIGHTING AND BEING A WARRIOR.
1833

I THINK I'LL BECOME A PECIS... A PACAS... A PASACIST... A CAPASIST... A PAT...

WHAT THE HELL— I'LL STAY A WARRIOR.

AH, THERE YOU ARE!
1834

I BRING YOU THE OLIVE BRANCH OF PEACE! FOR ME VIOLENCE IS A THING OF THE PAST.

PAY ATTENTION!
WHACK!

I OFFER YOU THE HAND OF FRIENDSHIP.
1835

IT'S TIME FOR TALKING, FOR DEEP AND MEANINGFUL DISCUSSION.

LEND US A QUID.

I'VE DRAWN UP THIS TREATY FOR YOU TO SIGN.
1836

ER... NO NEED TO READ IT— IT JUST SAYS THAT WE NOW RESPECT AND TRUST EACH OTHER.

"I AGREE TO PAY THE NOMAD £1,000."
BLUSH!

LET'S SHAKE HANDS.
1837

WE'RE FRIENDS AND ALLIES NOW.

NO MORE FIGHTING... NO MORE MISTRUST...
IF YOU'RE TRYING TO STEAL MY WATCH, IT'S ON THE OTHER WRIST.

RIGHT! THAT'S IT! THE TREATY'S OVER!
RIP!
1838

WE'RE NOW BACK AT WAR! PREPARE TO EAT STEEL!

HELP ME. I'VE CUT MY LEG AGAIN.

HERE COMES ANOTHER OF THOSE HUMANS.
1839

I WONDER IF HE'S ANY BRIGHTER THAN THE LAST ONE I MET.?

HALLO! A VOUCHER!

IT'S A TAME VOUCHER!
VULTURE, YOU IDIOT.
1840

I THOUGHT ALL VOUCHERS WERE WILD.
WILD? I'LL BE BLOODY FURIOUS IF YOU DON'T GET MY NAME RIGHT.

WOULD YOU LIKE SOMETHING TO EAT?
NO THANKS.
1841

I BET YOU WOULD!
I BET I WOULDN'T.

DO YOU LIKE CRISPS?
ONLY IF THEY'RE DEAD GOAT FLAVOURED.

YOU VOUCHERS ARE A CLEVER LOT.
1842

I NEVER KNOW HOW YOU MANAGE TO FIND YOUR PREY.

LOOK UP "DEAD GOATS" IN THE YELLOW PAGES.

HOW HUMANS CAME TO RULE THE WORLD I'LL NEVER KNOW.
1843

A QUIRK OF EVOLUTION, I SUPPOSE.

SPEAKING OF WHICH, THIS ONE LOOKS LIKE HE'S JUST MASTERED WALKING UPRIGHT.

WELL, I MUST GO ON DUTY NOW.
1844

NICE TO TALK TO YOU MR. VOUCHER.

IT'S AT TIMES LIKE THIS I REGRET NOT OWNING A HAND-GRENADE.

THE SERGEANT'S EXAM IS COMING UP AGAIN.
1845

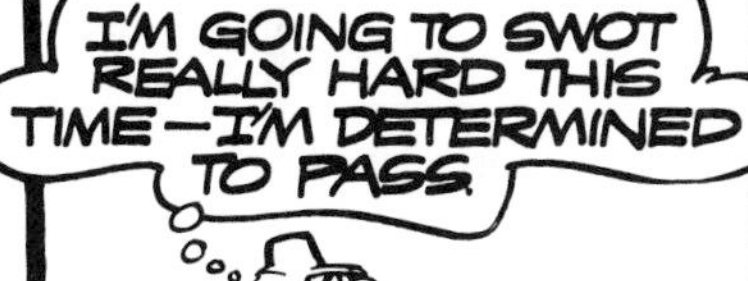
I'M GOING TO SWOT REALLY HARD THIS TIME—I'M DETERMINED TO PASS.

IT'S JUST A QUESTION OF HARD WORK AND COMMITMENT.

ANYONE FANCY A PINT?
COMING!

I CAN'T GO TO THE PUB, DENNIS.
WHY?
1846

BECAUSE I'M STUDYING FOR THE SERGEANT'S EXAM.

I REALLY WANT TO WEAR STRIPES, DENNIS.

D'YOU WANT MY PYJAMAS?

I'M SURE I'LL PASS MY SERGEANT'S EXAM THIS TIME!

I CAN HEAR THE SLEEVE OF MY TUNIC SHOUTING "SLAP THOSE OL' STRIPES ON ME, SARGE!"
1847

BEAU, I WAS—
DO YOU MIND? I'M TALKING TO MY SLEEVE!

WELL, HERE WE GO! TIME TO SIT MY SERGEANT'S EXAM!
1848
BE POSITIVE! THINK LIKE A SERGEANT! ACT LIKE A SERGEANT! BE CALM!
EVEN IF YOU'RE STANDING IN A BROOM CUPBOARD BY MISTAKE.

SERGEANT'S EXAM:—
FINAL QUESTION.

SELECT ODD ONE OUT AND GIVE REASON:—
COBRA, RATTLESNAKE, VIPER, BEETLE.
1849

WHAT A CINCH! IT'S "BEETLE"!

ALL THE OTHERS ARE COCKTAILS!

I HAVE THE RESULTS OF YOUR SERGEANT'S EXAM, PEEP.
YOU HAVE?

GIVE IT TO ME STRAIGHT, SARGE! ARE THESE ARMS TO BE WEARING STRIPES?
1850

NOT UNLESS YOU OWN A ZEBRA-SKIN COAT.

AHA! I'M SCOUTING WITH ACHMED THIS WEEK.
NOTICE
DUTY ROSTER
1851

I ENJOY THESE EXCURSIONS. I FEEL WE'VE DEVELOPED A MUTUAL RESPECT.

CAN'T SOMEONE ELSE GO? HE'S A PILLOCK.

YOUR NAME'S ACHMED, RIGHT?

DID YOU REALISE IT WAS AN ANAGRAM OF "ME CHAD"?

IT'S STRANGE— I HAVE THIS KNACK WITH WORDS.
1852

YOU HAVE THE KNACK OF BEING A PILLOCK.

FETCH ME THE ROUNDEST STONE YOU CAN FIND.
1853

THIS IS EXCITING! HE PROBABLY WANTS IT FOR SOME NATIVE TRICK TO FIND WATER!

DON'T BE STUPID—HOW CAN WE PLAY ROUNDERS WITH THAT?

YOU'RE A MAN OF THE DESERT, ACHMED—THERE'S SOMETHING THAT'S ALWAYS PUZZLED ME.
1854

WHAT CAUSES THAT SHIMMERING MIRAGE-LIKE EFFECT ON THE SAND?

DRINK.

A WOMAN IS COMING. SHE IS SMALL AND LIGHT.

SHE IS QUITE OLD AND LIMPS.

BRILLIANT! ALL THAT JUST BY LOOKING AT THE GROUND!
1855

WHAT? NO, NO—IT'S A POSTCARD FROM MY AUNTIE WILMA.

ALWAYS REMEMBER TWO THINGS...
1856

...THE DESERT IS YOUR GREATEST FRIEND AND YOUR DEADLIEST ENEMY.

OH, YES—AND SHORTBREAD KEEPS BETTER IN A TIN.

THE MIND IS A MARVELLOUS THING, DENNIS.
THE HUMAN BRAIN
1857

DID YOU KNOW THAT THERE ARE MILLIONS OF FACTS, FIGURES AND CONTROLS IN THERE?
THE HUMAN BRAIN

THE HUMAN BRAIN

TRY TO FIND THE BIT THAT WORKS YOUR MOUTH, DENNIS.
THE HUMAN BRAIN

IT SAYS HERE THAT THE BRAIN IS SPLIT INTO COMPARTMENTS.
THE HUMAN BRAIN

FOR EXAMPLE, ONE DEPARTMENT MIGHT HANDLE MATHEMATICAL PROBLEMS.
THE HUMAN BRAIN
1858

THE HUMAN BRAIN

COUNTING, DENNIS — YOU KNOW WHEN YOU STAMP YOUR HOOF.
THE HUMAN BRAIN

I WANT TO TRY AND EXPERIMENT IN TELEPATHY, DENNIS.
THE HUMAN BRAIN
1859

CONCENTRATE HARD AND TRY TO READ MY MIND. THIS COULD BE A GREAT MOMENT FOR SCIENCE!

YOUR NOSE HAS GONE ALL RED.

I'M SURE WE CAN GET THIS TELEPATHY THING TO WORK.
THE HUMAN BRAIN
1860

"IT IS IMPORTANT TO COMPLETELY CLEAR THE MIND."
THE HUMAN BRAIN

THE HUMAN

YOU CAN SAFELY SKIP THAT BIT, DENNIS.

PICTURE SOMETHING IN YOUR MIND, DENNIS, AND I'LL TRY TO PICK IT UP TELEPATHICALLY.
THE HUMAN BRAIN
1861
YES, YES... THAT'S IT... I FEEL IT COMING...
AMAZING! I CAN SEE THE GATES OF POMPEII... A ROMAN CENTURION... HIS TUNIC TORN AND BLOODIED...
I WAS THINKING OF A DUCK.

WHAT A BRILLIANT BOOK!
THE HUMAN BRAIN
1862
THE HUMAN BRAIN, DENNIS, WHO KNOWS WHAT IT IS CAPABLE OF?
DOES IT HAVE LIMITS? WHAT FRONTIERS OF INTELLECTUAL ADVENTURE LIE BEFORE US?
CAN I COLOUR IN THESE PICTURES?

I ENJOY A CHALLENGE!
HONEST ABDUL
1863

IF I CAN SELL ANY OF THIS JUNK I'LL TREAT MYSELF TO A NEW CART.
ST ABDUL

WHY DID YOU SAY "*HELLO, NEW CART*"?
DUL

I HAVE JUST THE THING FOR YOU!
HONEST ABDUL
1864

IT'S A PROTECTIVE TUNIC, COMPLETE WITH A MAGIC INSCRIPTION! NOTHING CAN HARM YOU WHILE YOU WEAR IT!

I FEEL SAFER ALREADY!
EAT AT JOE'S

HAH! THERE, YOU ARE!
EAT AT JOE'S
1865
YOUR BULLETS CAN'T HARM ME! I BOUGHT THIS MAGIC TUNIC FROM HONEST ABDUL!
EAT AT JOE'S
IT WILL PROTECT ME FROM KNIVES, SPEARS, CLUBS, BOMBS AND YOU'VE GOT THAT "YOU'VE BEEN DONE" EXPRESSION ON YOUR FACE.
EAT AT JOE'S

THERE ARE TWO REASONS WHY YOU'RE STILL VULNERABLE WEARING THAT THING.
EAT AT JOE'S
1866

ONE:- IT'S NOT A MAGIC TUNIC, IT'S A SANDWICH BOARD.

WHAT'S THE OTHER?
EAT AT JOE'S

SLAP!
EAT AT JOE'S

THIS IS A MAGIC TUNIC—BULLETS BOUNCE OFF IT!
EAT AT JOE'S
1867
I'M SO CONFIDENT, I'LL LET YOU FIRE AT ME. GO AHEAD—I HAVE COMPLETE FAITH.
EAT AT JOE'S
CLICK!
EAT AT JOE'S

TELL YOU WHAT—LET'S PUT IT ON A TREE.

ABDUL! JUST LOOK AT THIS "MAGIC PROTECTIVE TUNIC" YOU SOLD ME!
ST ABDUL
EAT AT JOE'S
1868

ER... YES... WELL, THERE IS ONE TYPE OF BULLET THAT CAN PENETRATE THE MAGIC.
DUL
EAT AT JOE'S

THAT WAS RAIN!

PEAS AND CARROTS ARE GOOD FOR YOU AREN'T THEY?
1869

VERY GOOD—IN FACT SOME PEOPLE SAY EATING VEGETABLES MAKES YOU CLEVER.

THAT'S IT— I'M GOING TO BECOME A **VEGETATION**!
CLICK!

WHY DO YOU WANT TO BE A VEGETARIAN?

'COS IT'S GOOD FOR YOU AND MAKES YOU CLEVER!
1870

CHOMP! I FEEL BRAINIER AFTER JUST ONE LETTUCE LEAF!

THAT'S A NAPKIN.

NO MEAT FOR DENNIS— HE'S BECOME A VEGETARIAN.
1871

HE RECKONS EATING VEGETABLES WILL MAKE HIM CLEVER.

THERE AREN'T THAT MANY VEGETABLES IN THE WORLD.

MENU
TODAY: BEEF AND CARROT STEW
1872

WILL YOU BE ABLE TO PREPARE VEGETARIAN MEALS FOR DENNIS?
OF COURSE.

GLOOP!

ONE CARROT STEW.

I FIND VEGETARIAN COOKING A REFRESHING CHALLENGE!
1873

WHAT'S *THIS*?

A SAUSAGE ROLL WITH THE SAUSAGE POKED OUT.

BEING A VEGETARIAN DOES MAKE YOU SMARTER.

I FEEL MUCH BRAINIER NOW.

BUT I'M PACKING IT IN 'COS I MISS EATING CHIPS.
1874

COLONEL ESCARGOT
COME!
1875

MORNING, SIR! GLAD TO HEAR YOU'RE BETTER, SIR!

GLAD TO HEAR YOU'RE BACK ON THE BALL AND THAT—
—YOU'RE IN A PENGUIN SUIT.

BRILLIANT, EH, PEEP? DRESSED LIKE PENGUINS WE CAN SPY ON THE ENEMY.

ER...DON'T YOU THINK IT WOULD LOOK A LITTLE SUSPICIOUS, SIR?

SUSPICIOUS, PEEP? SUSPICIOUS?
1876

NAME ME ONE PENGUIN WHO'S BEEN ARRESTED FOR SPYING!

BUT, SIR, IT JUST WON'T WORK!
IF WE TRY TO SPY ON THE ENEMY DRESSED AS PENGUINS, THEY'LL SIMPLY SHOOT US!

DON'T YOU THINK I'VE THOUGHT OF THAT? I'M NOT STUPID!
1877

IF THEY SHOOT US, WE REPORT THEM— PENGUINS ARE A PROTECTED SPECIES!

DRESSING AS PENGUINS IS CRAZY—THEY COME FROM THE ANTARCTIC NOT THE DESERT!
1878
YOU MEAN THE ENEMY HAVE NEVER SEEN ONE?
NEVER.
BETTER STILL! WE NAB THEM WHILE THEY'RE LOOKING US UP IN THE BIRD-WATCHER GUIDE!
COLONEL ESCARGOT
WHAT ARE YOU DOING, BEAU?
KLUNK! KLUNK!

I REGRET TO SAY, SIR, THAT I AM REFUSING AN ORDER.

I REFUSE TO DRESS AS A PENGUIN TO SPY ON THE ENEMY.
1879

YOU LEAVE ME WITH ONLY ONE OPTION, PEEP!
FUMBLE!

THE BARNACLE GOOSE!

I'VE CALLED OFF MY PLAN TO SPY ON THE ENEMY DRESSED AS PENGUINS.

A WISE DECISION, SIR— IT WOULD NEVER HAVE WORKED.

WELL, I DIDN'T WANT TO RISK THE MEN'S LIVES.
1880

ANYWAY, I NEED THE EGGS.

ONCE AGAIN, IT IS TIME TO AWARD THE YEAR'S MEDALS.

EARL BRAUN, WHO DEFENDED A POSITION SINGLE-HANDED.

FOR BRAVERY UNDER ENEMY FIRE, JAN LARSON.

...LUIGI CAPALDI, HEROISM BEYOND THE CALL OF DUTY.

AND, LAST BUT NOT LEAST, BEAU PEEP...

...SPELLING AND DICTATION.

YOU NEVER GET LOST WITH OLD ACHMED!

LOOK AT THAT — HE'S CHECKING OUR POSITION WITH THE STARS...

...SCANNING THE SKIES FOR OUR BEARING.

I WONDER WHAT PRIMITIVE INSTINCT FIRST MADE MAN LOOK UPWARDS FOR GUIDANCE.

HE'S TREMBLING WITH EXCITEMENT! HE MUST HAVE FIXED OUR POSITION!

THAT'S BETTER! I HAD SOME SAND DOWN MY NECK.

ONE, TWO, THREE... ER... FOUR!

WHEE! UP THE LADDER!

1583
BINK! BONK! BINK! BONK! OH, NO! A BIG BAD SNAKE!

ZOOM! ALL THE WAY BACK DOWN! THUMP!

I DON'T THINK YOU'LL EVER GET THE HANG OF CHESS.

IT CAN BE VERY EERIE ON NIGHT DUTY.

I THINK IT'S TO DO WITH THE DESERT WIND.

SOMETIMES, WHEN IT HOWLS, IT SOUNDS VERY GHOST-LIKE.

WOOOOOOH!

JUST LIKE THAT! IT SOUNDS LIKE THE CRY OF A LOST SOUL, DOOMED FOREVER TO WANDER THE SPIRIT WORLD.

WOOOOOH! AM I DRUNK!

BAD NEWS, PEEP.

ONE OF OUR NEW TOP-SECRET RIFLES IS MISSING.

DO YOU REALISE WHAT THAT MEANS?

IT MEANS THAT SOMEWHERE OUT THERE THE ENEMY HAS OUR NEW RIFLE!

TAKE MY WORD FOR IT— THEY'RE SMART. THEY'LL KNOW HOW TO USE IT!

FORE!

THIS IS YOUR FIRST FIGHT, PIERRE, SO START CAUTIOUSLY.

DODGE AND WEAVE FOR A COUPLE OF ROUNDS TO SIZE HIM UP.

LET HIM THROW A COUPLE OF PUNCHES TO CHECK HIS STRENGTHS.

TREAT HIM WITH RESPECT AND I'LL WORK OUT THE TACTICS FOR LATER ROUNDS.

DING! DING!

OR, ALTERNATIVELY, BEAT HIM TO A PULP IN 30 SECONDS.

I'VE GOT A GREAT IDEA—
A COMPETITION!
THUD!

YOU SEE THIS SACK
OF POTATOES?
YES.

WELL, IF YOU GUESS
THE NUMBER OF
POTATOES IN IT...

...I'LL COOK YOU
A SLAP-UP MEAL
OF YOUR CHOICE!

ONE.

PEOPLE HAVE AN IMAGE OF THE LEGION, PEEP?

THEY EITHER SEE US AS CUT-THROATS AND REFUGEES FROM THE LAW...

...OR ROMANTIC ESCAPISTS TRYING TO FORGET A WOMAN.

EITHER WAY, IT'S A STRONG, MANLY IMAGE.

WHAT ARE YOU TRYING TO SAY, SARGE ?

OUR REQUEST FOR A NEEDLEWORK CLUB HAS BEEN TURNED DOWN.

EVENING, PEEP.

OH... ER... EVENING, SARGE!

WHAT WERE YOU LOOKING AT YOUR WATCH FOR? YOU'RE SUPPOSED TO BE GUARDING THIS GATE!

IF I THOUGHT FOR ONE MINUTE YOU WERE NEGLECTING YOUR DUTY...
ME, SARGE?

NOT ME! I FULLY REALISE THE SERIOUSNESS AND RESPONSIBILITY OF THE JOB!

DID YOU TIME ME, BEAU? ONCE ROUND THE FORT IN MY KNICKERS!

ASTRO
THE SOOTHSAYER
WELCOME SEEKER OF TRUTH.

TO LEARN ABOUT YOU I MUST *BECOME YOU*!

I'M GOING TO PROJECT MYSELF INSIDE YOUR MIND, INSIDE THE LIVING-ROOM OF YOUR VERY BRAIN!

YOU COULD DO WITH SOME FURNITURE.

HALT! WHO GOES THERE?
IT'S ME—DENNIS.

YOU'VE GOT TO SAY "FRIEND OR FOE."
"FRIEND OR FOE"

NO, NO, YOU'VE GOT TO SAY ONE OR THE OTHER.

WHAT DOES "FOE" MEAN?
YOU KNOW—IT'S A SORT OF ENEMY.

A "SORT OF ENEMY" WHAT, LIKE A NEIGHBOUR OR SOMEONE YOU DON'T LIKE?

...SO IS IT OKAY IF HE JUST ANSWERS "IT'S ME DENNIS."

TAKE A DEEP BREATH AND RELAX.
1468

THE SARGE WILL NEVER KNOW I'M DRUNK IF I KEEP MY WITS ABOUT ME.

HEAD HELD HIGH AND WALK IN A STRAIGHT LINE!

I'LL JUST SAY GOOD NIGHT AND GO STRAIGHT PAST.

G'NIGHT, SARGE!
GOOD NIGHT, PEEP.

...AND THEN I WAS SO HAPPY I'D GOT OFF WITH IT, I WENT BACK AND KISSED HIM ON THE NOSE.

NICE NIGHT, DENNIS.

I SAID, "NICE NIGHT, DENNIS."

DENNIS? WHAT ARE YOU DOING?
MUTTER!

SEVEN!

IT'S SEVEN!
WH-WHAT IS?

THAT FIRST QUESTION IN MY 11-PLUS!

THIS IS THE LIFE—FAR FROM THE HEAT OF THE KITCHEN!
1462

NO COMPLAINTS ABOUT MY COOKING...

...NO OLD JOKES ABOUT CRUEL COOKS WHO BEAT EGGS AND WHIP CREAM!

WHAT BLISS TO BE FAR AWAY FROM THE INSULTS AND JIBES!

DON'T TELL ME —CORN SOUP!

TELL YOU WHAT, DENNIS— I'LL TEST YOU WITH AN OLD BRAIN-TEASER!
1456

A MAN IS LOOKING AT A PORTRAIT AND HE SAYS "BROTHERS AND SISTERS HAVE I NONE..."

...BUT THAT MAN'S FATHER IS MY FATHER'S SON." WHO IS HE LOOKING AT?

IT'S ALMOST AS THOUGH THERE'S BEEN SOME SORT OF EXPLOSION IN HIS HEAD.
INFIRMARY

MAY I SUGGEST HOW WE CONFRONT THE ENEMY, SARGE?

WE GROUP THE MEN TOGETHER HERE...

...THEN WE MARCH OFF IN ONE FORCE...

...ALL DAY AND ALL NIGHT IF NECESSARY.

BUT, PEEP—THE ENEMY ARE GROUPED HERE. WE'D BE MILES AWAY.

DAMN RIGHT

IF YOU FOLD YOUR HANKIE LIKE THIS...

...YOU GET A LITTLE BUNNY-RABBIT!
BRILLIANT!
1881

IF I WERE HIM, I'D BE TRYING TO FOLD MYSELF A COUPLE OF BRAINS.

A VULTURE!
1882

THEY HAVE A FASCINATING UGLINESS...A HYPNOTIC APPEARANCE OF EVIL!

LISTEN TO CLARK GABLE.

WHAT A MORBID EXISTENCE YOU LEAD...
...PREYING ON THE WEAK AND DYING.
DO YOU BLAME ME?
I ONCE LANDED ON A DOBERMAN —DAMN THING WAS ONLY SLEEPING— NEARLY LOST MY LEG.
1883
I WONDER HOW INTELLIGENT VULTURES ARE?
PRETTY STUPID I SHOULD THINK.
I AGREE...
...THEN AGAIN, I'M NOT THE ONE IN A SILLY HAT TALKING TO A BIRD.
1884

IF ONLY BIRDS AND ANIMALS COULD TALK.
1885

I'M SURE WE'D LEARN A LOT. I WONDER WHAT THEY'D SAY?

NOT A LOT – I'D BE TOO BUSY LAUGHING AT YOUR HAT.

IT'S STRANGE THE WAY HE JUST SITS THERE.
1886

MOST VULTURES ARE SHY, TIMID CREATURES.

MOST VULTURES HAVEN'T HAD A BOTTLE OF SHERRY.

WE MUST FIND OUT WHAT THE ENEMY IS UP TO.
1887

THE FIRST LEGIONNAIRE WE SEE, WE WILL CAPTURE AND TORTURE!

THE SECOND LEGIONNAIRE WE SEE WE WILL CAPTURE AND TORTURE.

HERE COMES ONE NOW!
1888

WE'LL NIP OUT AND GRAB HIM THEN, USING SUBTLE TORTURE, BRAINWASH HIM!

HARDLY WORTH WASHING.

WE SHALL HAVE TO THINK OF A SPECIAL TORTURE!
1889

IT'S ALMOST IMPOSSIBLE TO GET A LEGIONNAIRE TO TALK!

SORRY, I COULDN'T HELP OVERHEARING BUT, ACTUALLY, ONE OR TWO OF US ARE RIGHT LITTLE CHATTERBOXES!

I'VE GOT IT! I'LL UPROOT THIS TREE, BASH 'EM OVER THE HEAD WITH IT AND ESCAPE!
1890

THIS'LL HAVE 'EM TERRIFIED!

DO YOU NEED THE TOILET?

WHAT IS IT TO BE—
TALK OR TORTURE?
1891

THERE'S ONLY ONE ANSWER TO THAT, YOU SWINE!

YOU'LL TALK?
LIKE A BUDGIE!

SO YOU MANAGED TO ESCAPE FROM THE ENEMY, PEEP?
YES, SIR.

THERE ARE TWO WAYS TO DO THAT, PEEP. YOU FIGHT YOUR WAY OUT...
1892

...OR YOU GIVE THEM INFORMATION!

THOSE ARE NICE CURTAINS—ARE THEY NEW?

I DON'T BELIEVE IT— MY LONG-LOST BROTHER!
1893

DESTINY HAS THROWN US TOGETHER AGAIN!

THE BLOOD WHICH RUNS THROUGH OUR VEINS FORMED A BOND NEITHER TIME NOR DISTANCE COULD BREAK!

I SEE YOU'VE STILL GOT A BIG NOSE.

MY HEART SOARS TO SEE YOU AGAIN, MY BROTHER!
1894

FORGIVE THIS FOOLISH TEAR— YOU MUST HAVE SPENT YEARS COMBING THE DESERT FOR ME.

ACTUALLY, I'M LOOKING FOR A SWEETIE SHOP.

HOW ARE OUR PARENTS, MY BROTHER?
1895

DO THEY STILL THINK OF THEIR LONG-LOST SON?

EVERY NIGHT—THEY HAVE BETS ON WHO CAN REMEMBER YOUR NAME.

WELL, I MUST BE OFF!
1896

YOU CANNOT LEAVE, MY BROTHER!

WE HAVEN'T MET FOR YEARS! THERE MUST BE SO MUCH YOU WANT TO ASK ME!

OH, YES— WHERE'S MY MARBLE?

THIS IS FROM OUR PARENTS.
1897

THEY SAID I SHOULD GIVE IT TO YOU IF WE MET.

SNIFF! I-I'VE NEVER BEEN SO MOVED.

DAMN! THE SPRING STUCK—THAT SHOULD HAVE PUNCHED YOU ON THE NOSE!

FAREWELL, MY BROTHER!
1898

GIVE MY LOVE TO OUR PARENTS—THEY'LL BE RELIEVED TO KNOW I'M WELL.

IN CASE THEY ASK, WHAT IS YOUR NAME AGAIN?

WHAT ARE YOU DOING, BEAU?
1899

I'M WRITING TO A VERY EXCLUSIVE PEN-PAL CLUB.

IT'S FOR PEOPLE WHO WISH TO EXCHANGE VIEWS ON MEANINGFUL TOPICS.

GET ME A GIRL WITH A BIG CHEST!

Dear Pen-Pal,
1900

Let me first tell you of my interests.

Classical music, art...in short anything tasteful.

HERE, BEAU– I FOUND YOUR NAKED GIRLIE TIE!

and that, dear pen-pal, wraps up my first letter.
1901

the foundation of a new relationship has been laid.

a foundation based on truth.

Best wishes, Colonel Beau Peep

HAVING PEN-PALS IS STUPID!
1902

IT'S A CULTURAL THING, DENNIS.

TO SHARE THINGS WITH PEOPLE ON A SIMILAR INTELLECTUAL LEVEL.

WHY DON'T YOU WRITE TO A SHOAL OF HADDOCK?

I'VE GOT A LETTER FROM MY NEW PEN-PAL.
1903

IT'S GREAT TO BE IN TOUCH WITH THE CULTURAL WORLD...

...AND WITH SOMEONE WHO CAN WRITE WITH FLAIR AND STYLE...

...IN CRAYON.

THIS PEN-PAL CLUB WAS SUPPOSED TO BE EXCLUSIVE!
1904

IT WAS FOR INTELLECTUAL AND STIMULATING EXCHANGES OF OPINIONS.

HOW CAN ANYONE SPELL "PEN" WRONG?

I THOUGHT WE'D GO INTO TOWN TONIGHT, DENNIS...
GREAT!
1905

...HAVE A FEW DRINKS, A NICE MEAL...
TERRIFIC!

...AND YOU PAY YOUR SHARE.
I'VE GOT A HEADACHE.

YOU BUY THE FIRST ROUND, DENNIS.
WHAT!
BAR

DON'T BE SO MEAN, DENNIS! I WANT YOU TO GO STRAIGHT UP TO THAT BAR AND ORDER A ROUND!
1906

I'LL GET YOU A GLASS OF WATER, DENNIS, BUT I'M NOT BUYING THE DRINKS.

PROVE TO ME YOU'RE NOT MEAN, DENNIS—BUY THE FIRST ROUND!

CAN I HA... CAN I HAVE...
1907

CAN I HA...HA... CAN I...

...CAN I PLEASE GO HOME, BEAU?

OKAY! OKAY! I'LL BUY THE FIRST ROUND! I'M NOT MEAN!
1908

WHAT DO YOU WANT?
A HALF OF BEER.

WHAT, A *FULL* HALF?

I HOPE YOU ENJOY THAT BEER – IT COST ENOUGH!

DON'T FORGET IT'S YOUR ROUND NEXT!
1909

I WASN'T LEAVING, DENNIS, I WAS GOING TO THE TOILET.

YOU ARE THE MEANEST PERSON ALIVE, DENNIS!
BAR

ON YOUR ROUND, YOU HAD NOTHING – ON MINE, YOU HAD A BOTTLE OF WINE AND THREE BEERS!
1910

THAT'S A POINT – YOU FORGOT MY CRISPS!

THE SECRET OF A GOOD MEAL IS BALANCE.

ONE COURSE MUST BALANCE WITH THE OTHER.
1911

TODAY, WE HAVE DUCK IN ORANGE SAUCE.
WHAT'S THE PUDDING ?

AN ORANGE IN DUCK SAUCE.

YOU SEE, I'M AN ARTIST IN THE KITCHEN.
1912

YOUR SOUP CERTAINLY TASTES LIKE PAINT.

THAT'S VERY AMUSING. ARTIST... PAINT... VERY GOOD.

I'VE GOT THE CARROT OUT OF HIS NOSE BUT I CAN'T REACH THE SAUSAGE.
INFIRMARY

Dear Mr Ritz,
I'd like to work in your Hotel.
1913

I have enclosed one of my recipes.

I'LL GO AND SEE ASTRO THE SOOTHSAYER.
1914

HE'LL TELL ME IF I'M DESTINED TO BECOME A WORLD-FAMOUS CHEF.

AT LEAST, HE'LL TREAT ME WITH RESPECT.

AHA! A ONE-EYED LOONY APPROACHES!

LETTERS ARE FORMING...

C...H...E...

CHEF! THAT'S IT! I'LL BE A GREAT CHEF!
1915

HANG ON — IT'S A CHEWING-GUM WRAPPER STUCK ON THE BALL.

WILL I COOK FOR ROYALTY?

HAVE MY OWN RESTAURANT? BE A FAMOUS CHEF?
1916

PLEASE DON'T SAY NO!

HOW ABOUT IF I USE THE WORD "BOTTOM" INSTEAD OF THE WORD "NO"?

AHA! MY ONE AND ONLY TRUE FRIEND!
1917

YOU DON'T CARE IF I'M TALL, SHORT, THIN OR FAT.

ACTUALLY, DEAD AND PLUMPISH ARE MY FAVOURITES.

I'M SURE I COULD TRAIN THIS VULTURE.
1918

I COULD REWARD HIM FOR EVERYTHING HE LEARNS.

NOW YOU'RE TALKING— ONE DEAD GOAT AND I'M ANYBODY'S.

I WONDER WHAT I COULD TRAIN HIM TO DO?
1919
MAYBE I COULD TEACH HIM TO CATCH RABBITS.
THAT'S A THOUGHT...

...A FEW TRAPS WOULD BE QUITE USEFUL.

PRETEND THIS NEWSPAPER IS A RABBIT.
VERY LIFELIKE.
1920

NOW FETCH IT!

IT'S WORKING! HE UNDERSTANDS!

JUST CHECKING THE PAPER. IT'S ALL RIGHT—I'VE READ IT.

I'LL DRAG THIS PRETEND RABBIT BEHIND ME.
NEWS
1921

A BIT OF MOTION WILL MAKE IT MORE REALISTIC.
INDEED IT DOES...

...YOU NOW LOOK EXACTLY LIKE AN IDIOT WITH A PAPER RABBIT.

I'VE GOT IT! I'LL TEACH YOU TO DROP BOMBS ON THE FORT!
1922

THERE'S A SNAG TO THIS...

...IF I SPOT A HERD OF GOATS FIRST, I KNOW WHERE THE BOMB'S GOING.

HERE COMES MAD PIERRE—I'M ON DUTY WITH HIM THIS WEEK.
1923

WELL, HE'S GOING TO MEET A NEW ME—ONE WHO REFUSES TO BE BULLIED.

I'LL GIVE YOU A POUND IF YOU DON'T HIT ME!

PIERRE, WHY DO YOU ALWAYS WANT TO HIT ME?
1924
YOU'RE SMALL, FAT, UGLY, STUPID, FOUR-EYED, ANNOYING...ER... DID I SAY "UGLY"?
YES.
THAT'S ANOTHER THING—YOU'VE ALWAYS GOT AN ANSWER.

I'VE JUST HAD A BRILLIANT IDEA!

IF I ASK MAD PIERRE TO HIT ME, HE WON'T BECAUSE THAT WOULD TAKE ALL THE FUN AWAY!

HIT ME!
WHACK!
1925

BRILLIANT IDEAS HURT MY HEAD.

LET ME ASK YOU A QUESTION, PIERRE...

...IS THERE ANYTHING I CAN DO TO STOP YOU HITTING ME?

WHACK!
1926

STOP ASKING QUESTIONS.

IT'S SO SIMPLE I DON'T KNOW WHY I DIDN'T THINK OF IT BEFORE!

EVERY TIME I OPEN MY MOUTH, PIERRE HITS ME—SO ALL I HAVE TO DO IS KEEP QUIET!

WHACK!
1927

I HATE SILENCE.

HOW WAS YOUR WEEK WITH MAD PIERRE?
OH, GREAT.
1928

...HE HITS ME WHEN I TALK AND HITS ME WHEN I DON'T. HE HITS ME WHEN I'M CLOSE...

KLUNK!

...AND THROWS STONES WHEN I'M NOT.

THIS WEEK WE'RE GOING TO DISCUSS FIRST AID.
FIRST AID
1929

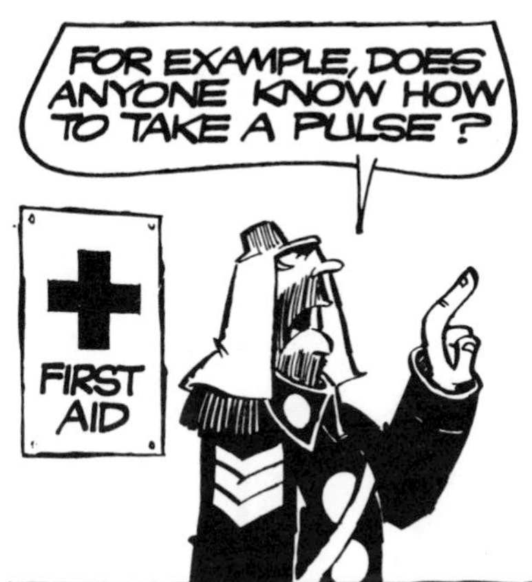
FOR EXAMPLE, DOES ANYONE KNOW HOW TO TAKE A PULSE?
FIRST AID

PINCH IT WHEN SHE'S NOT LOOK—
PULSE, DENNIS, NOT PURSE.

WE'RE GOING TO PRACTICE THE "KISS OF LIFE."
FIRST AID
1930

I WANT EACH OF YOU TO FIND A PARTNER.

REMEMBER, KNOWING THIS ROUTINE, COULD SAVE SOMEONE'S LIFE.

YOU'RE DEAD.

RIGHT, LET'S CONTINUE WITH THE FIRST AID CLASS.
FIRST AID
1931

WE'LL PRETEND I HAVE A BROKEN LEG. WHAT SHOULD I DO FIRST?
FIRST AID

FALL OVER.

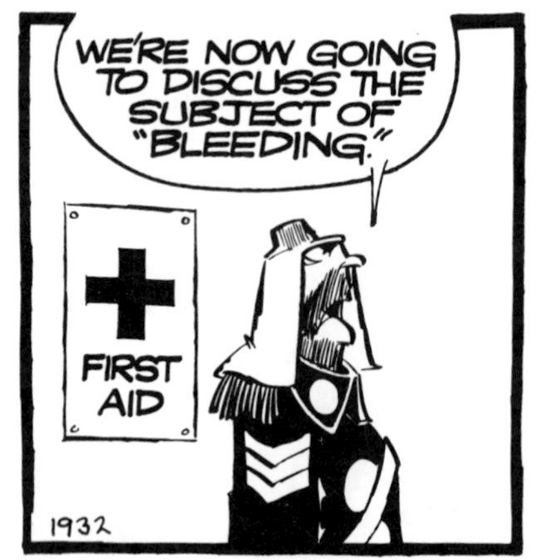
WE'RE NOW GOING TO DISCUSS THE SUBJECT OF "BLEEDING."
FIRST AID
1932

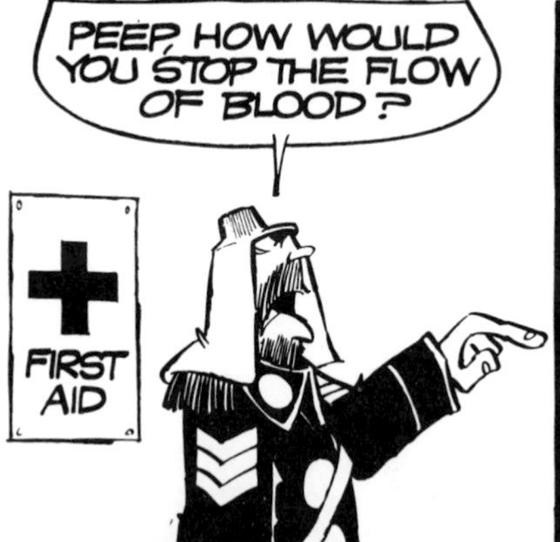
PEEP, HOW WOULD YOU STOP THE FLOW OF BLOOD?
FIRST AID

ASK MAD PIERRE TO STOP HITTING ME.

I NEED A VOLUNTEER— PRATT, STEP FORWARD.
FIRST AID
1933

PRETEND I'VE BROKEN MY ARM. NOW, LET'S SEE YOU MAKE A SLING.

A MINUTE OF YOUR TIME, PRATT...

I HAVE HERE THE RESULTS OF YOUR WRITTEN FIRST AID EXAM.
FIRST AID
1934

MOST OF YOU HAVE GRASPED THE BASICS AND SHOULD BE ABLE TO COPE WITH THE MORE STRAIGHTFORWARD MEDICAL PROBLEMS...

...EXCEPT FOR PEEP WHO SHARPENED HIS PENCIL FOR THE TEST, CUT HIS FINGER, SAW THE BLOOD AND PASSED OUT.

WHAT ARE YOU THINKING ABOUT, DENNIS?
1935

HUNDREDS OF NAKED WOMEN WITH BIG CHESTS CHASING ME ALONG A BEACH.

AND HERE WAS ME WONDERING WHAT'S FOR TEA.

DENNIS, WHAT WOULD YOUR IDEAL WOMAN BE?
1936

HERE.

WOMEN ARE WONDERFUL CREATURES, DENNIS!
1937

THEY SAY A GOOD WOMAN IS LIKE A BOTTLE OF THE FINEST WINE!

I KNOW WHAT YOU MEAN — I CAN'T GET THEIR TOPS OFF.

I ALWAYS REMEMBER MY FIRST GIRLFRIEND...

...THE FIRST KISS, THE HINT OF A BLUSH, THE SHEER INNOCENCE OF IT ALL.
1938

DO YOU REMEMBER YOURS?
YES...

...I SWAPPED HER FOR A HEDGEHOG.

CAN I GIVE YOU A TIP ABOUT WOMEN, DENNIS?
YES.
1939

NOTHING PLEASES THEM MORE THAN TO HEAR THOSE THREE MAGIC LITTLE WORDS.

WHAT, ABRACADABRA?

I'LL REMEMBER THOSE TIPS YOU GAVE ME ABOUT WOMEN!
GOOD.

THEY'RE REALLY SURPRISING, SOME OF THEM.
1940

I CAN'T GET OVER THEM NOT LIKING SLUGS!

THE SERGEANT WANTS US TO SELL VESTS AND PANTS!
WHAT?
1941

YEAH! HE SAYS WE'RE TO BE UNDERWEAR AGENTS!

UNDERCOVER AGENTS?
CLICK!

IT'S VERY SIMPLE— YOU GO BEHIND ENEMY LINES AND SPY.. ANY QUESTIONS?
1942

WHISPER.

WHY DON'T YOU LIKE US?

YOU WANT US TO SPY BEHIND ENEMY LINES?
YES.

BUT WE'LL BE SO CONSPICUOUS DRESSED LIKE THIS!
1943

YOU AND YOUR BIG MOUTH!

BEING DRESSED LIKE THE ENEMY ISN'T ENOUGH, DENNIS!
1944

WE MUST BE THEM! WE MUST BE AT ONE WITH THE DESERT—AS THOUGH IT'S BEEN OUR LIFE!

HANG ON—I'VE GOT SAND IN ME WELLIES!

OUR LIFE DEPENDS ON FOOLING THE ENEMY, DENNIS.
1945

WE MUST EAT, SLEEP AND BREATHE JUST LIKE THEM!

IS THE JAM ROLY-POLY READY?

IF ANYONE APPROACHES, DON'T TALK.
1946

IF THEY ASK A QUESTION, ANSWER WITH A SIGN.

DON'T BE SMUTTY, DENNIS.

SOMEONE'S COMING! KEEP CALM AND LET ME DO THE TALKING!
1947

DON'T PANIC. WE'LL BE ALL RIGHT. REMAIN COOL. THINK POSITIVE.

LET'S SHOOT OURSELVES.

GREETINGS.
ER...GREETINGS!
1948
I AM SEEKING TWO SPIES AND WHEN I FIND THEM I WILL CHOP THEIR EARS OFF.
HE DOESN'T RECOGNISE US! OUR DISGUISES FOOLED HIM!

YOU LOOK LIKE OUR SERGEANT AT THE FORT!

DO YOU KNOW WHAT I DO WITH SPIES?
NO.

PERHAPS YOU WOULD LIKE ME TO TELL YOU?
1949

WHISPER

NO.

DON'T WORRY, DENNIS—I'LL GET US OUT OF THIS!
1950

LOOK OVER THERE!

HA! TAKE THAT, SUCKER!
BOP!

HELP ME FIND MY KNUCKLES, DENNIS.

I WONDER HOW PEEP AND PRATT ARE DOING?

I HOPE THEY REMEMBER THE LEGION MOTTO— "DEATH BEFORE DISHONOUR"
1951

THAT'S IT SETTLED THEN—YOU LET US GO FOR A WATCH, TWO BAGS OF SWEETS AND A PHOTO OF "NAUGHTY NANCY."

WE'RE BACK, SERGEANT!
1952

A SUCCESSFUL UNDERCOVER JOB COMPLETED, SIR!

THE DESERT IS LITTERED WITH THE BODIES OF THOSE WHO TRIED TO STOP US!

WE RAN OVER AN ANT-HILL!

WHAT ON EARTH WILL I DO WITH THESE PLUNGERS I BOUGHT?
HONEST ABDUL
1953

IT WAS STUPID OF ME— I'LL NEVER FIND AN IDIOT TO BUY THEM.

BOY, WAS I LUCKY TO BUY HONEST ABDUL'S LAST "HUMAN FLY" KIT!

WHAT A GENIUS I AM!
1954

WITH THIS "HUMAN FLY" KIT I CAN SCALE THE WALL AND SLAUGHTER THE SENTRIES!

SLIDE!

DID YOU HEAR SOMEONE SAY "MUMMY"?

THE HUMAN FLY MOVES SILENTLY UPWARDS!
1955

OH-OH...

POP! POP! POP! POP! MUMMY! WHUMP!

DO YOU EVER GET THE FEELING THAT SOMETHING ODD IS GOING ON?

WHAT ARE YOU DOING?
1956

I'M A HUMAN FLY AND YOU CAN'T STOP ME NOW!

WHAP!

BET?
WHUMP!

PUFF! PANT! NEARLY THERE!
WHAT TIME IS IT?
1957

IT'S... ER... LET'S SEE...

DAMN.

LIKE SHELLING PEAS.
WHUMP!

WHY DO MY DEVIOUS PLANS NEVER SUCCEED?
1958

WELL, ONE DID BUT THAT WAS A LONG TIME AGO.

IN THE END, HER MUM MADE ME GIVE HER BACK HER DOLL.

I PACKED MY SUITCASE...
WHAT?
1959

IT'S A MEMORY GAME. YOU LIST ALL THE THINGS YOU PUT IN A SUITCASE AND TRY TO REMEMBER THEM.

REMEMBER WHAT?

I PACKED MY SUITCASE AND PUT IN A TOOTHBRUSH...
1960

GO ON—YOU SAY SOMETHING NOW.

HELLO!

DENNIS, IT'S VERY SIMPLE...
...AFTER YOU SAY "I PACKED MY SUITCASE" WE EACH ADD TO A LIST OF THINGS.
1961

THEN, ONCE YOU GET TO ABOUT TWENTY THINGS IT GETS DIFFICULT!

WHAT, TO CLOSE THE CASE?

I PACKED MY SUITCASE AND PUT IN MY SLIPPERS...
SO DID I.
1962

NO, YOU'VE GOT TO ADD SOMETHING DIFFERENT.

BUT I NEED MY SLIPPERS.

WHAT YOU NEED IS A TEN YARD START— I'M GOING TO CHOKE YOU.

I THINK I'VE GOT THE HANG OF THE GAME NOW.
1963

I PACKED MY SUITCASE AND PUT IN MY PYJAMAS.

AT LAST! RIGHT, NOW I ADD ANOTHER ITEM!

HANG ON, WILL I TAKE THE ONES WITH RABBITS OR TRAINS?

I HAVE TRIED UNSUCCESSFULLY TO TEACH YOU A VERY SIMPLE GAME.
1964

RELUCTANTLY, I HAVE REACHED THE CONCLUSION YOU HAVE THE INTELLIGENCE OF A STICK INSECT.

I CAN SEE MYSELF IN YOUR GLASSES.

OOH, WHAT A NIGHT ON THE TOWN THAT WAS!

I DON'T REMEMBER A THING ABOUT IT— I HOPE I DIDN'T DO ANYTHING STUPID!
1965

SO THERE YOU ARE! YOU'D BETTER TURN UP FOR OUR DUEL AT MIDDAY.

HOW COULD I DO IT?
WHAT?

LAST NIGHT I WAS DRUNK AND I CHALLENGED MAD PIERRE TO A DUEL!
1966

WHAT WILL I DO?
DIE HORRIBLY.

IT'S A NOTE FROM MAD PIERRE!

"FOR OUR DUEL I RECOMMEND SWORDS BUT YOU MUST CHOOSE."
1967

"CURRANT BUNS"?

RIGHT, IT IS DECIDED— WE WILL FIGHT WITH SWORDS.
1968

WE WILL FOLLOW THE STRICT RULES OF DUELLING— DO YOU HAVE A SECOND?

SURE—TAKE AS LONG AS YOU LIKE!

MAD PIERRE WILL GET A SHOCK WHEN HE DISCOVERS I'M A MASTER SWORDSMAN!
1969

HA-HA! DON'T LIKE THE TASTE OF COLD STEEL, EH?
SWISH!

WHAT HAPPENED?
YOU SLICED THROUGH YOUR SHORTS TRIPPED OVER THE ELASTIC AND KNOCKED YOURSELF OUT.

WHAT HAPPENED TO YOU, THEN?

IT WAS STUPID—I WENT AND CHALLENGED MAD PIERRE TO A DUEL.
1970

PISTOLS?
I'D CERTAINLY HAD A FEW.

MORNING, BEAU!
MORNING, DENNIS.
1971

HAVE YOU, BY ANY CHANCE, BEEN AT HONEST ABDUL'S?
YES, HOW DID YOU KNOW?

A WILD GUESS.

HOW COULD YOU DO IT, DENNIS?
1972

HOW COULD YOU LET HONEST ABDUL CON YOU INTO BUYING SKIS?
SKIS?

OH, YOU MEAN MY *GUARANTEED MONEY-DETECTORS*!

HONEST ABDUL SOLD ME THESE MONEY-DETECTORS!
1973

HE SAID THAT IF I WALK OVER ANY BURIED MONEY THEY'LL VIBRATE.

HOW APPROPRIATE THAT HE SOLD YOU TWO SHORT PLANKS.

MY MONEY-DETECTORS ARE VIBRATING!
1974

DENNIS, THOSE ARE SKIS!
THEN WHY ARE THEY VIBRATING?

I DON'T KNOW— SOMETIMES THE BRAIN SENDS OUT VIBRATIONS!

THOUGH, I THINK WE CAN SAFELY RULE THAT OUT IN YOUR CASE.

YOU MEAN THESE AREN'T MONEY-DETECTORS?
NO...
...THEY'RE SKIS, DENNIS. HONEST ABDUL HAS CONNED YOU.
I DON'T SUPPOSE I'LL NEED MY "POUND-NOTE-PICKER-UP."
1975

REMEMBER, DENNIS, LET ME DO THE TALKING.

WITH THESE PEOPLE, POLITENESS IS EVERYTHING...

...SO DON'T SPEAK UNLESS YOU'RE SPOKEN TO.

GREETINGS
GREETINGS.

THIS IS MY COMRADE, DENNIS, WHO...

...HAD TO POINT OUT THE WART ON THE BIG ONE'S NOSE.

I WAS JUST THINKING BACK TO WHEN I WAS A BOY.
OH, YES?

MY DAD TOOK ME EVERYWHERE WITH HIM.

HE WAS REALLY PROUD OF ME, HE WAS!

HE WOULD TELL EVERYONE, "THIS IS MY SON, DENNIS..."

I WONDER HOW ALIKE DENNIS AND HIS DAD ARE?
SLURP!

"...AND ONE DAY HE'LL BE A FAMOUS STURGEON!"
TWO PEAS.

WOULD YOU READ THIS LETTER FROM MY MUM?
SURE.
1589

DEAR DENNIS, WENT TO THE ZOO YESTERDAY...

...AND SAW A BIG BIRD CALLED A BEAGLE...

...ALSO SOME MONKEYS CALLED BUFFOONS. CHEERIO, PET.—MUM.

DEAR OLD MUM! SHE ALWAYS GETS THINGS MIXED UP!

IT'S MY BROTHER HECTOR SHE CALLS 'PET'!

ACHMED'S MAKING A FIRE.
1595

I LOVE WATCHING HIM WORK! SUCH ARTISTRY!

AND NOW DINNER— ANOTHER TRADITIONAL DELICACY!

SLIVERS OF MEAT ROASTED OVER AN OPEN FIRE! DELICIOUS!

A RECIPE THAT'S PROBABLY AS OLD AS THE DESERT ITSELF!

ARE MY SOCKS DRY YET?

YOU DEAL SOME SWEET PASTEBOARDS, BABY!
PARDON?

GIVE ME TWO CARDS!
DENNIS, I...

GIVE ME TWO CARDS, BUSTER!

FLIP!
FLAP!

YOUR THOUSAND PLUS ANOTHER THOUSAND TO SWEETEN THE POT!

DENNIS, DO YOU WANT TO LOOK AT THESE POSTCARDS OR DON'T YOU?

My Dearest Darling Doris,
163

I love you very much.

every day without you is torture.

I dream only of the time you are in my arms again.

HI, BEAU—WHAT ARE YOU DOING?

I'VE GOT AN UPSET STOMACH—I'M TRYING TO MAKE MYSELF SICK.

HO!! FOUREYES! CATCH THIS!

"UNLESS YOU ALL SURRENDER I WILL BOMBARD THE FORT."

"I HAVE A TERRIBLE NEW SECRET WEAPON..."
1547

..."WHICH IS SO DEADLY THAT..."
OH, HANG ON A MINUTE...

...COULD YOU GIVE ME MY STONE BACK?

RIGHT, PEEP. IT'S YOU AGAINST THE CLOCK.

WHEN I GIVE YOU THE WORD YOU DROP TO THE GROUND...

...AND GIVE ME 30 PRESS-UPS AS QUICKLY AS YOU CAN.

I'LL TIME THEM — GO!

27...28...29...

...30! AFTER ONE PRESS-UP, YOU WERE UNCONSCIOUS FOR 30 SECONDS.